Science

SCIENCE
Quest

CHANGING STATE

CONTENTS

SOLIDS, LIQUIDS & GASES

The three states of matter

All matter can exist as a **solid**, as a **liquid** or as a **gas**.

Make a list of the names of some solids, liquids and gases.

Air is made up of a mixture of gases:
Nitrogen   78%
Oxygen   21%
Other gases   1%

Water is a liquid. It also exists as a solid called ice and as a gas called steam or water vapour.

Most of the Earth's crust is solid rock.

The hot rock beneath the Earth's crust exists in liquid form.

All matter is made up of **particles** which are in a constant state of motion. This motion increases as the temperature rises. The arrangement of particles is different in solids, liquids and gases. Forces between the particles tend to hold them together while the motion caused by heat tends to move them apart.

A solid has a definite shape and a definite volume. The particles in a solid are held closely together by the forces between them. The motion caused by temperature is sufficient for the particles to vibrate but not break apart.

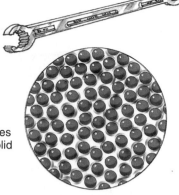

Particles in a solid

Are solids easy or hard to squash?

Do you think the forces between the particles in a solid are strong or weak?

A liquid has no definite shape but does have a fixed volume. It flows to fill a container from the bottom up. In a liquid the particles are held close together, but have sufficient energy to slide around each other in any direction.

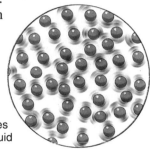

Particles in a liquid

How does the shape of a liquid change when you pour it from a bottle into a glass?

Do you think the forces of attraction between the particles in a liquid are stronger or weaker than they are in a solid? Explain your answer.

A gas has no definite shape and expands to fill the whole of its container. It can occupy any volume. The particles in a gas have so much energy that they have broken away from the forces holding them together.

What happens to the particles when a gas is squashed?

Why is a gas easy to squash?

Particles in a gas

SUMMARY
Substances exist in three states – solid, liquid and gas.

The particles are arranged differently in solids, liquids and gases.

The forces of attraction are strong in solids, weaker in liquids and weakest in gases.

MELTING & FREEZING
How solids turn into liquids, and back again

This diagram shows the particles in a lump of chocolate. The particles are arranged in a well-ordered pattern. The particles vibrate slightly in all directions but not enough to break free of the forces which hold them in place.

When the chocolate is heated, the particles gain more energy. Their vibrations become stronger and they can move more freely but cannot escape the forces which hold them in position.

At a certain temperature, the particles vibrate so much that they break free of the forces which hold them in place. The well-ordered pattern breaks down and the chocolate becomes liquid.

How does the arrangement of particles differ between solid and liquid chocolate?

What will happen to the chocolate if its particles vibrate more strongly?

What word describes what happens when a solid turns into a liquid?

Hot liquid chocolate can be poured. Chocolate bars are made by pouring liquid chocolate into moulds. As the liquid cools the particles lose energy and they vibrate less and less. At a certain temperature, there is not enough energy for the particles to remain as a liquid and they change back to a solid. This temperature is called the **freezing point** and is different for each liquid.

What word describes what happens when a liquid turns into a solid?

The temperature at which a solid turns into a liquid is called its **melting point**.

The underneath and front of the space shuttle is covered with ceramic tiles which have a high melting point. They protect the spacecraft from heat during re-entry.

Some substances have low melting points. Some substances have high melting points.

Mercury is a metal which is liquid at room temperature. It has a low melting point of −39 °C.

In a substance with a low melting point the forces between the particles are weak and the particles can break free at a low temperature. In a substance with a high melting point the particles are held together very strongly. More heat is needed to break the attractive forces between the particles.

Tungsten has a high melting point of 3380 °C. It is used for the filament in electric bulbs.

Scientists can sometimes identify an unknown substance by finding its melting point and comparing this to a list of known melting points. However if the substance contains impurities this will lower the melting point.

Substance	Melting point	Appearance
Silver	2180 °C	
Copper	1083 °C	
Aluminium	660 °C	
Sulphur	445 °C	

If an unknown substance has a melting point of 659 °C, what could the substance be, and do you think it is pure?

Why is salt put on icy roads in freezing weather?

SUMMARY
When a solid melts, it turns to a liquid.
When a liquid freezes, it turns to a solid.
Different substances have different melting points and freezing points.
Impurities in a substance lower the melting point.

EVAPORATION
How liquids turn into gases and back again

When a liquid is at a constant temperature not all the particles have the same energy. They bump into each other causing some to move faster and some slower.

On the surface of a liquid some of the faster particles have enough energy to break free into the space above. The escaping particles at the surface of the liquid become gas. This process is called **evaporation.**

In the middle of a liquid the few particles moving fast enough to form a gas soon collide with other particles. They slow down again and remain as liquid.

If heat is added, the energy of the particles increases and more and more of them move faster.

If enough heat is added even the particles in the middle of a liquid move so fast that they break free from the forces which hold them. This is called **boiling**.

The temperature at which a liquid boils is called its **boiling point.**

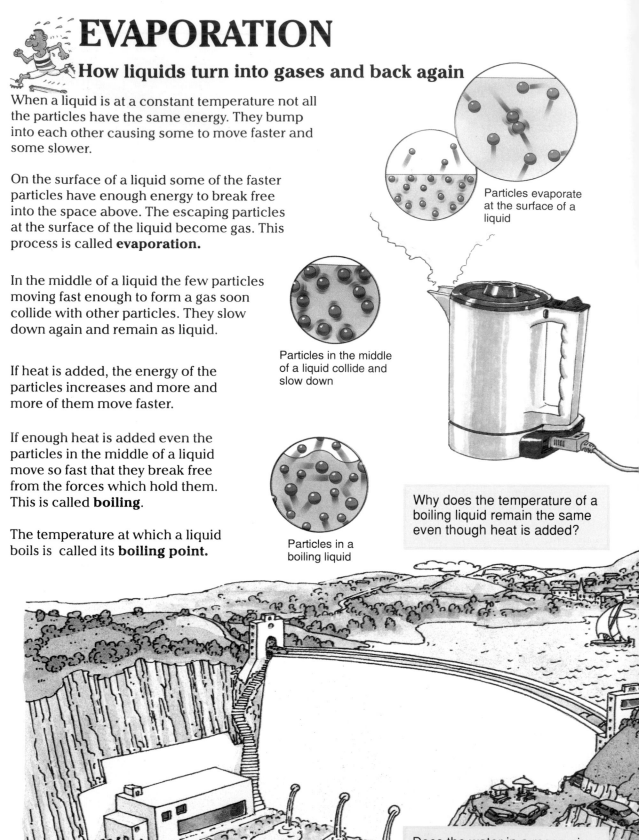

Particles evaporate at the surface of a liquid

Particles in the middle of a liquid collide and slow down

Particles in a boiling liquid

Why does the temperature of a boiling liquid remain the same even though heat is added?

Does the water in a reservoir evaporate more quickly on a hot day or a cold day?

When the boiling point has been reached, heat added to the liquid is completely taken up in freeing the particles from each other to become gas. The temperature of the liquid does not rise any more.

Different liquids have different boiling points. The boiling point of water is 100°C. The boiling point of ethanol is 78°C.

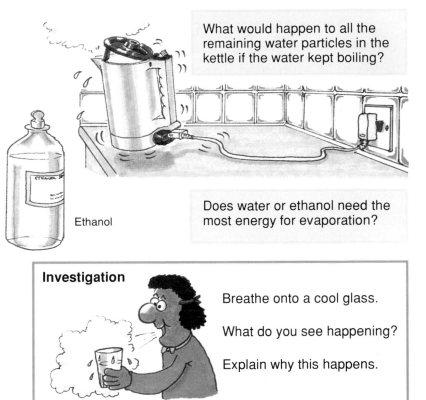

Ethanol

What would happen to all the remaining water particles in the kettle if the water kept boiling?

Does water or ethanol need the most energy for evaporation?

Once the gas particles have left the liquid, they may begin to lose energy. If they lose enough energy by being cooled, these gas particles return to their liquid state. This process is called **condensation**.

When water vapour cools it loses energy and **condenses** back into water.

Investigation

Breathe onto a cool glass.

What do you see happening?

Explain why this happens.

Devise a test to show how the speed of evaporation of a liquid is affected by its surface area.

Devise a simple experiment to test your prediction.

The water in this reservoir is evaporating all the time. Part of the water vapour rises to form clouds. The clouds are blown towards the cool hills where the vapour condenses and falls as rain. The rain-water returns to the reservoir. This is called the water cycle.

SUMMARY
When a liquid evaporates, it changes to a gas.
When a gas condenses, it changes to a liquid.
Different liquids have different boiling points.

ENERGY

The role of energy during melting and evaporation

The particles in ice are held together in a crystal pattern by strong attractive forces.

Adding heat energy makes the particles vibrate. At first the ice particles retain their solid structure and the temperature rises.

When the ice reaches melting point, its temperature stops rising. Instead, the heat energy is absorbed by the particles and is used to break the forces of attraction between them.

When the ice has melted, the temperature of the water will once more begin to rise as the heating continues.

The quantity of heat energy required to convert a solid to a liquid is called the **latent heat of fusion**.

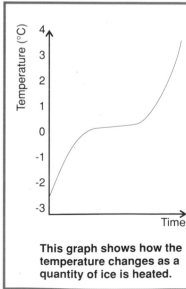

This graph shows how the temperature changes as a quantity of ice is heated.

What do you notice about how the temperature rises? Why does the temperature stay at 0 °C for a while?

8

When heat energy is given to a liquid, its particles move faster and faster.

When the liquid reaches its boiling point, its temperature does not continue to rise. Instead, the added energy makes the particles break free from the liquid and form a gas.

The energy needed at the boiling point of a liquid to completely free the particles from each other is called the **latent heat of vaporization**.

When a liquid evaporates it absorbs heat and when it condenses it gives out heat. A fridge uses this principle to transfer heat from inside the fridge to the outside.

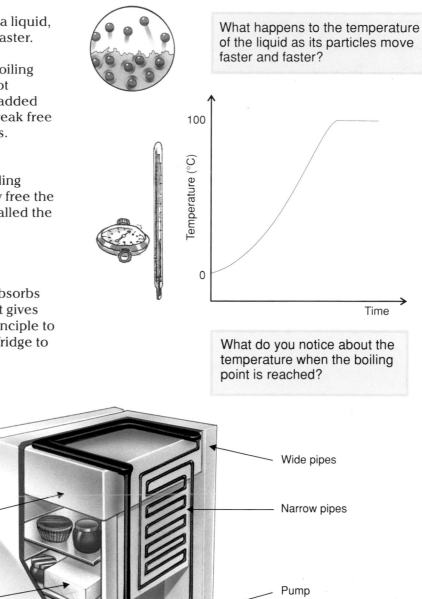

What happens to the temperature of the liquid as its particles move faster and faster?

What do you notice about the temperature when the boiling point is reached?

Cut-away of a fridge

What effect will the evaporation of the freon have on the temperature inside the ice box?

A liquid called a coolant is pumped into wide pipes round the ice box. Here, it expands and evaporates and absorbs heat from inside the fridge. The coolant is then pumped into the narrow pipes at the back of the fridge where it is compressed. It condenses back to a liquid and releases its heat energy. It then returns to the pump.

Substances called freons are used as coolants because they have very low boiling points.

SUMMARY

When a substance is heated, melts or evaporates, it absorbs energy.

When a substance is cooled, condenses or freezes, it loses energy.

GASES I

Pressure and temperature

The amount of matter in a substance is called its **mass** and is measured in kilogrammes. Gases have mass. Blowing up a balloon fills it with air.

This balloon has a mass of 10 g. After it's inflated the balloon has a mass of 13 g.

What is the mass of the air inside the balloon?

Inside the balloon the gas particles are moving around freely in all directions. The particles hit the skin of the balloon and each other. When they hit the skin of the balloon they exert a **pressure**.

The air particles outside the balloon also exert a pressure.

What happens to the skin of the balloon when the gas particles hit the inside of the balloon?

The pressure on the outside of the balloon is equal to the pressure on the inside.

Pressure is sometimes measured in units called **millimetres of mercury (mm Hg).**

What would happen if there was more pressure on the inside of the skin than the skin could withstand?

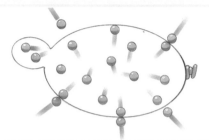

When a balloon is filled with helium gas, gravity acting on the helium particles in the balloon is less than that which would act on air filling the same shape. This makes the balloon lighter than air and it rises.

If all the air were sucked out of this empty can, there would be less pressure on the inside compared to the outside.

If the balloon were filled with air instead of helium, would it have a greater or lesser mass?

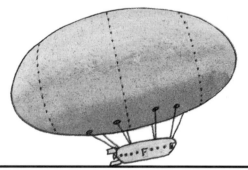

What would happen to the can if the air were sucked out? Why?

The particles in a gas move very fast. When the gas is heated, the particles take in energy and move faster. They hit the walls of a container more often and with more force. This causes the pressure to increase.

When water is boiled under pressure, the particles need more energy to escape from the liquid and form steam. This means that the boiling point rises. A pressure cooker uses this principle so that food can be boiled at a higher temperature.

Temperature can be measured in units called degrees **centigrade.** The temperature at which water freezes is 0 degrees centigrade (0°C). The temperature at which water boils is 100°C. Temperature can also be measured in **Kelvin.** This scale begins at the lowest possible temperature – called **absolute zero.** On this scale water freezes at 273 Kelvin (273 K) and water boils at 373 K.

A working pressure cooker contains steam under very high pressure.

Explain why increasing the temperature of a gas increases the pressure the gas exerts.

This diagram shows the relationship between centigrade and Kelvin scales

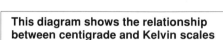

Absolute zero	Freezing point of water		Boiling point of water
-273°	Centigrade	0°	100°
0°	Kelvin	273°	373°

The Kelvin scale is named after Lord William Kelvin (1824–1907), a scientist who investigated gases.

This graph shows how the pressure of a gas changes with temperature

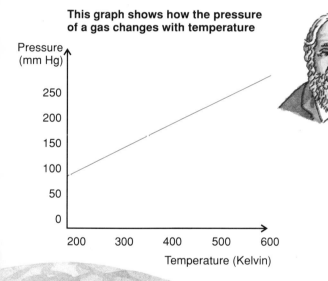

What happens to the pressure of a gas when the temperature is doubled? Using this graph, if the temperature of the gas is 500 K, what temperature would it have to cool down to in order to halve the pressure?

Car tyres can become very hot during a long, fast journey. Why is it best to check the pressure in car tyres after they have cooled down?

SUMMARY
Gases have a mass.
Gases exert pressure.
When the temperature of a gas increases, the pressure it exerts also increases.

GASES II

Pressure, volume and temperature

If a gas is **compressed** so that its volume decreases the gas particles are forced closer together. Because they are closer together they exert more pressure on the walls of the vessel containing them. The petroleum gas in a petrol engine is compressed by pistons which move inside gas-tight cylinders.

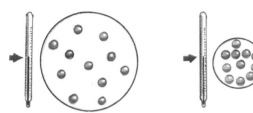

If the pressure on a gas is increased, the volume will decrease in proportion, provided that the temperature remains constant. We say that the volume of a gas is **inversely proportional** to the pressure exerted on it.
This relationship was discovered by Robert Boyle (1627–91) and is known as Boyle's Law.

What happens to the volume of the gas when the particles are forced closer together?

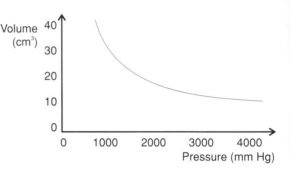

If the volume of the gas is increased, will its pressure increase or decrease? Explain why.

Compressed air is used in a variety of machines such as factory robots and pneumatic drills. A motor-driven compressor pulls in air, compresses it and pipes it to where it is needed.

Why do you think compressed gases are more useful for making machines work than uncompressed gases?

When a gas cools, its pressure is reduced. This is because the gas particles have less energy and press less strongly on the walls of the container.

If a gas is cooled down enough, it condenses into a liquid.

Gas bottles used in compact, portable heaters contain pressurized gas in liquid form.

Why is it useful to be able to store gases in liquid form?

How would you describe the sort of container needed to hold pressurized liquid gas?

Gas

Paint

Perfume

Some aerosol cans contain a pressurized gas mixed with a product such as perfume. Pushing the nozzle releases the mix of gas and perfume. The released gas expands rapidly and turns the liquid perfume into a fine spray.

Other aerosol cans are designed to release a thicker spray of a product such as paint. In this case the gas and the paint don't mix. When the nozzle is pushed, the pressurized gas above the paint forces the paint from the can. The gas remains under pressure in the can until most of the paint has gone.

Why do you think the gas released from an aerosol can is usually very cold?

SUMMARY

When the pressure on a gas increases, its volume decreases.
When the pressure on a gas decreases, its volume increases.
When the temperature of a gas increases, its pressure increases.
When the temperature of a gas decreases, its pressure decreases.

13

EXPANSION & CONTRACTION

How things change size when heated or cooled

This metal ball goes through the metal ring.

When the same ball is heated it will not go through the ring.

This is how the particles in the cold ball are arranged.

What happens to the spacing between the particles when the ball is heated? How will this affect the size of the ball?

Why will the hot ball not go through the ring? There are two ways to get the ball to go through the ring. Describe them both.

Engineers have to be careful to take expansion and contraction into account when they build things.

What happens to these wires when the weather is cold?

These telegraph wires are very slack because the sun is making them hot.

Lengths of railway track are placed with gaps between the lengths of steel to allow room for them to expand.

What would happen if there were no gaps between the railway tracks?

Trains have steel tyres. Suggest how steel tyres are fitted to steel train wheels.

Different materials expand by different amounts when heated. This is due to the different structure of the particles from which they are made and the different way they are affected by heat. A **bimetallic strip** is made from lengths of two different metals bonded together. When the bimetallic strip is heated, the two different metals expand by different amounts. This makes the strip bend.

Bimetallic strip

Which of the two metals in this bimetallic strip is expanding the most? Why do you think this?

The temperature in an oven needs to be kept steady. A bimetallic strip is used in an electric oven to control the temperature. A device for maintaining a selected temperature is called a **thermostat**.

As the oven heats up, the bimetallic strip bends away from the contact. When the oven is at the required temperature the electrical contact is broken and the oven stops heating.

What happens to the bimetallic strip when the oven reaches the selected temperature?

What then happens to the oven temperature?

What then happens to the bimetallic strip?

Engineers must allow for the expansion and contraction of metal in bridges.

Suggest how this might be done.

SUMMARY
Particles move away from each other as an object is heated.
Objects expand as they are heated.
Particles move towards each other as an object is cooled.
Objects contract as they are cooled.
Different materials expand and contract by different amounts.

DISSOLVING
How solids and gases become part of a liquid

Many solids and gases can **dissolve** in liquids. When a solid dissolves, the structure of the particles changes and they act more like the particles of the liquid. For example solid salt has particles which are held in a rigid structure. When salt is dissolved in water, the particles become free to move around amongst the water particles.

Many liquids can dissolve substances and are called **solvents**. For example methanol can dissolve sugar.
Some substances dissolve in water. Substances which dissolve easily in water are said to be **soluble.** Carbon dioxide and chlorine gas are both soluble in water.

Swimming pool water contains chlorine gas which helps to kill germs.

The bubbles in fizzy drinks are dissolved carbon dioxide gas escaping from the liquid.

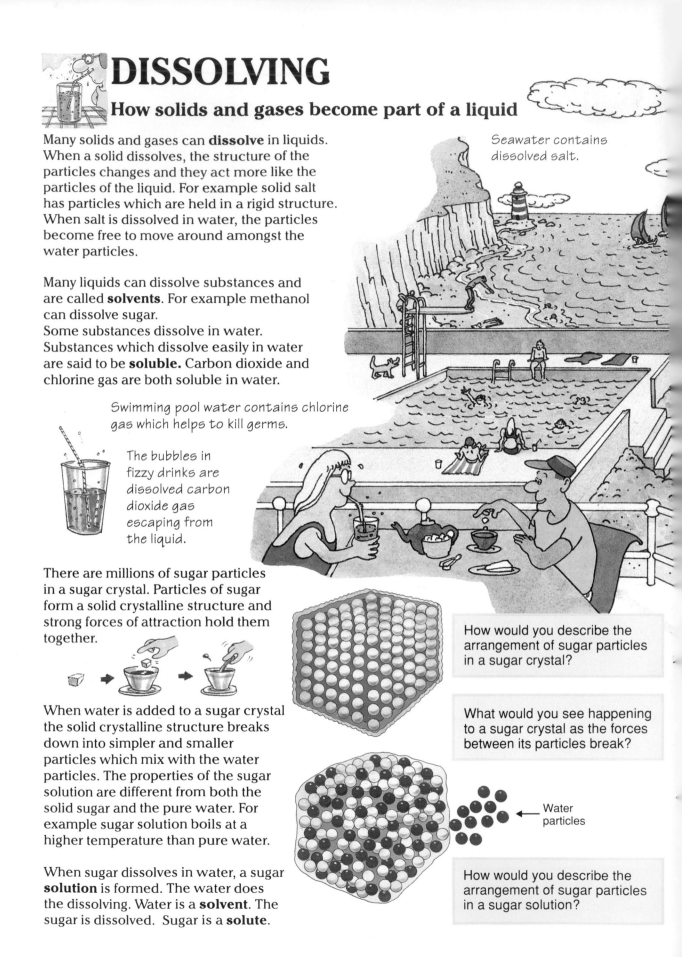

Seawater contains dissolved salt.

There are millions of sugar particles in a sugar crystal. Particles of sugar form a solid crystalline structure and strong forces of attraction hold them together.

When water is added to a sugar crystal the solid crystalline structure breaks down into simpler and smaller particles which mix with the water particles. The properties of the sugar solution are different from both the solid sugar and the pure water. For example sugar solution boils at a higher temperature than pure water.

When sugar dissolves in water, a sugar **solution** is formed. The water does the dissolving. Water is a **solvent**. The sugar is dissolved. Sugar is a **solute**.

How would you describe the arrangement of sugar particles in a sugar crystal?

What would you see happening to a sugar crystal as the forces between its particles break?

Water particles

How would you describe the arrangement of sugar particles in a sugar solution?

Some substances are more soluble than others.
Sea water contains dissolved sodium chloride
and potassium sulphate.

Investigation

If you were given solid samples of
sodium chloride and potassium
sulphate, how would you find out
which is the most soluble in water?

Some substances do not easily
dissolve in water. These substances
are said to be **insoluble.**

Is sand soluble or insoluble?
Why do you think this?

How strong do you think the attractive
forces must be beween the particles in
a grain of sand?

Investigation

Sugar   Granulated   Icing
cube   sugar   sugar

Which of these types of sugar do you
think will dissolve the quickest?
Can you explain why?

What might affect the speed at which
each type of sugar dissolves?

How would you test your predictions?

SUMMARY

Substances which dissolve in liquids
are soluble.

Substances which do not dissolve in
any liquids are insoluble.

When a solution is made, the forces
between solute particles are broken
and new forces between solute and
solvent particles are formed.

DIFFUSION

How the particles of different substances mix

Smoke particles are much bigger than particles of air but they are still too small to be seen under a normal microscope. If a light is shone through smoke under a microscope, tiny bright points of light can be seen moving about. This is light reflected by the smoke particles. The points of light are moving because the smoke particles are being bombarded by small, fast-moving air particles.

This movement is called **Brownian motion**. The same effect can be seen with liquids.

Particles in a gas are constantly moving, making the gas as a whole spread out. When two separate gases are brought together the movement of their particles tends to cause the gases to mix into each other. This process is called **diffusion**. The particles from each gas follow their own random movement. Diffusion of a gas is how a smell travels through still air.

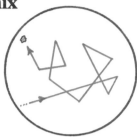

The path a smoke particle in a gas might follow

Where on its path has this smoke particle been hit by air particles?

In 1827 the scientist Robert Brown was the first to notice the movement of visible particles in a gas or liquid when they are hit by smaller particles. He was observing pollen grains in water.

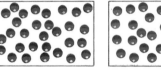

Using your knowledge of particles and diffusion, explain how the smell of flowers or of sausages reaches your nose.

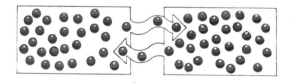

Diffusion also occurs between liquids. For example, if a spot of red food colouring is added to water and left for a while, the water turns red as the particles in the food colouring mingle with the particles in the liquid.

A solid can diffuse into a liquid, too. This is what happens when solutes are dissolved by solvents.

Why does the water all eventually change colour when the red colouring is added?

Investigation

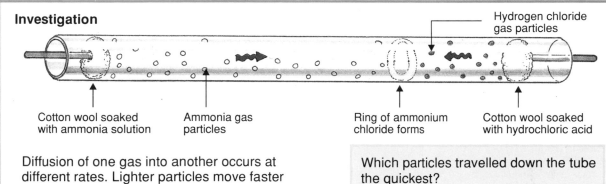

Hydrogen chloride gas particles

Cotton wool soaked with ammonia solution

Ammonia gas particles

Ring of ammonium chloride forms

Cotton wool soaked with hydrochloric acid

Diffusion of one gas into another occurs at different rates. Lighter particles move faster than heavier ones. Above, the ammonia and hydrogen chloride particles meet up and form a white ring of ammonium chloride. This ring is nearest to the acid end of the tube.

Which particles travelled down the tube the quickest?

Where would you expect the ring to form if the tube were gently heated at the hydrochloric acid end? Explain why.

SUMMARY
Brownian motion is the movement of particles after being hit by other particles. Diffusion is the spreading of particles from one substance into another. The rate of diffusion is increased if heat is applied to the particles.

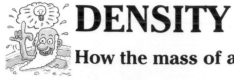

DENSITY

How the mass of a substance is related to its volume

The volume of a rectangular solid can be calculated using the equation:

Volume = Length × Breadth × Width

The units of volume are cubic metres (m^3) or cubic centimetres (cm^3).

The density of an object is defined as its mass per unit volume and can be calculated using the equation:

Density = Mass ÷ Volume

The units of density are kilogrammes per cubic metre (kg/m^3) or grammes per cubic centimetre (g/cm^3).

Gold has a high density because the particles are heavy and very closely packed. The density of gold is $19.3\,g/cm^3$.

This gold ring may have copper as an impurity mixed in with the gold. The ring has a mass of 20 g and a volume of $1.5\,cm^3$.

When an object is added to this can of water, some of the water will flow out of the spout.

3 cm
5 cm
4 cm

What is the volume of this gold bar?

This gold bar has a mass of 570 g and a volume of $30\,cm^3$. What is its density?

The density of copper is $8.9\,g/cm^3$ and the density of gold is $19.3\,g/cm^3$. How could you determine whether the ring is pure gold or has impurities in it?

The greek philosopher Archimedes (287–212BC) was in the bath when he discovered how to determine the purity of gold.

How could you find the density of an irregularly shaped object?

The density of an object depends on two things: the mass of the particles and how close the particles are packed together.

Aluminium cans are lighter than steel cans.
This is how the particles are arranged in the steel can.

How do the particles in the aluminium compare those in the steel?

Which of these two squashed cans has the highest density?

Most gases have a low density. Why do you think this is?

When a gas is heated its particles move further apart. How does the temperature of a gas affect its density?

What effect does compacting have on the density of the materials?

What could happen to roads if the road materials were not compacted enough?

When engineers build roads the materials they use have to be **compacted** which means they are squashed into a smaller volume.

SUMMARY
Density = Mass ÷ Volume
Density depends on the mass of the particles and how closely the particles are packed together.

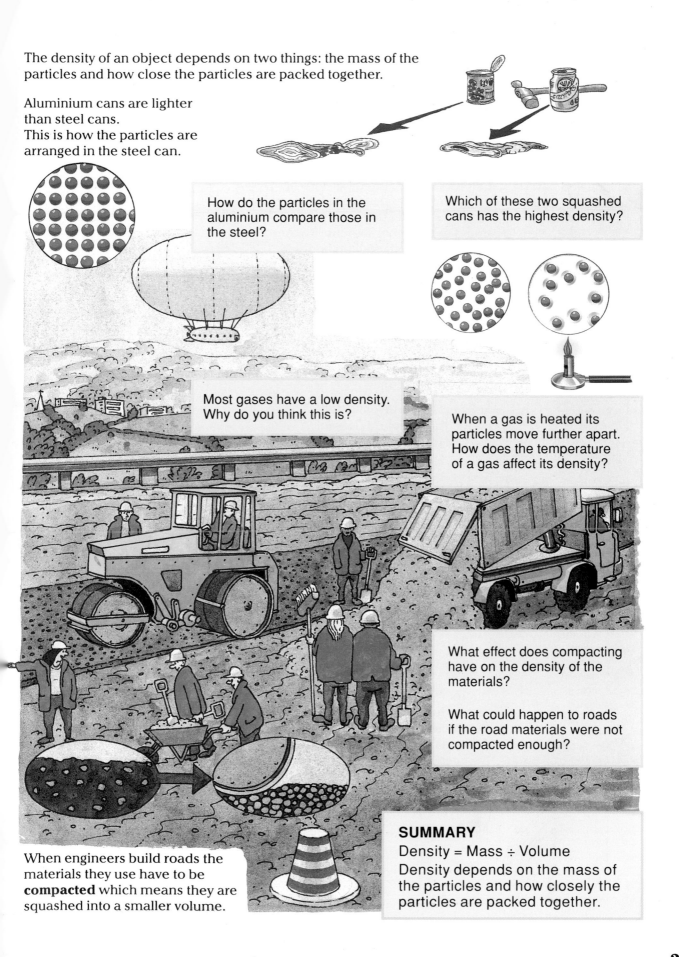

ELEMENTS & THE ATOM
Different elements have different atomic structures

Table of elements		
No.	Element	Symbol
1	Hydrogen	H
2	Helium	He
3	Lithium	Li
4	Beryllium	Be
5	Boron	B
6	Carbon	C
7	Nitrogen	N
8	Oxygen	O
9	Fluorine	F
10	Neon	Ne
11	Sodium	Na
12	Magnesium	Mg
13	Aluminium	Al
14	Silicon	Si
15	Phosphorous	P
16	Sulphur	S
17	Chlorine	Cl
18	Argon	Ar
19	Potassium	K
20	Calcium	Ca
21	Scandium	Se
22	Titanium	Ti
23	Vanadium	V
24	Chromium	Cr
25	Manganese	Mn
26	Iron	Fe
27	Cobalt	Co
28	Nickel	Ni
29	Copper	Cu
30	Zinc	Zn
31	Gallium	Ga
32	Germanium	Ge
33	Arsenic	As
34	Selenium	Se
35	Bromine	Br
36	Krypton	Kr
37	Rubidium	Rb
38	Strontium	Sr
39	Yttrium	Y
40	Zirconium	Zr
41	Niobium	Nb
42	Molybdenum	Mo
43	Technetium	Tc
44	Ruthenium	Ru
45	Rhodium	Rh
46	Palladium	Pd
47	Silver	Ag
48	Cadmium	Cd
49	Indium	In
50	Tin	Sn
51	Antimony	Sb
52	Tellurium	Te
53	Iodine	I

Elements are the simplest building blocks from which all chemicals are made. Many of them combine together to form the thousands of different substances we see around us. For example, table salt is made from the elements sodium (Na) and chlorine (Cl). But sodium and chlorine can also exist as separate elements on their own.

There are 105 different known elements. Ninety-two of these are natural and found on Earth. The other elements are artificially produced.

Scientists have investigated elements and found uses for most of them.

Scientists group elements together in different ways, for example metals and non-metals.

Gold (metal)

Iron (metal)

Aluminium (metal)

Oxygen (non-metal)

Sulphur (non-metal)

Bromine (non-metal)

Another way of grouping elements is as **conductors and non-conductors**. Conductors allow electricity to pass through them, non-conductors don't. Non-conductors are also called **insulators.**

Metals are good conductors. Most non-metals are good insulators.

Mercury

Nickel

Some advertising signs are filled with neon gas which lights up when an electric charge is passed through.

Tantalum is a metal which can be used to replace parts of the skull because it is so corrosion-resistant and strong.

Name some other metallic elements.

Name some other non-metallic elements.

Phosphorus

Helium

Copper

Knowing that metals conduct electricity well and other elements don't, which of these elements do you think are electrical insulators?

The smallest part of an element is called an **atom.** All the atoms of an element are the same as one another, but they differ from the atoms of all other elements.

Atoms are made up of even smaller particles. These are **protons, neutrons** and **electrons.**

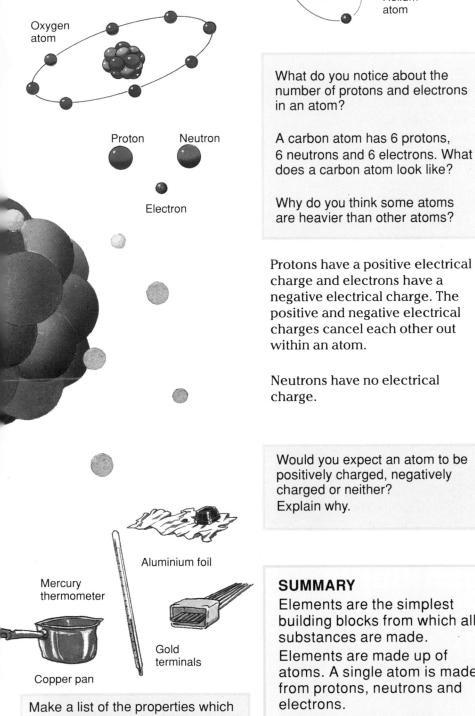

Hydrogen atom

Helium atom

Oxygen atom

Proton   Neutron

Electron

What do you notice about the number of protons and electrons in an atom?

A carbon atom has 6 protons, 6 neutrons and 6 electrons. What does a carbon atom look like?

Why do you think some atoms are heavier than other atoms?

Protons have a positive electrical charge and electrons have a negative electrical charge. The positive and negative electrical charges cancel each other out within an atom.

Neutrons have no electrical charge.

Would you expect an atom to be positively charged, negatively charged or neither? Explain why.

Aluminium foil

Mercury thermometer

Gold terminals

Copper pan

Make a list of the properties which are needed for each of these metal objects to perform usefully.

SUMMARY
Elements are the simplest building blocks from which all substances are made.
Elements are made up of atoms. A single atom is made from protons, neutrons and electrons.
Different elements have different properties.

Table of elements		
No.	Element	Symbol
54	Xenon	Xe
55	Caesium	Cs
56	Barium	Ba
57	Lanthanum	La
58	Cerium	Ce
59	Praseodymium	Pr
60	Neodymium	Nd
61	Promethium	Pm
62	Samarium	Sm
63	Europium	Eu
64	Gadolinium	Gd
65	Terbium	Tb
66	Dysprosium	Dy
67	Holmium	Ho
68	Erbium	Er
69	Thulium	Tm
70	Ytterbium	Yb
71	Lutetium	Lu
72	Hafnium	Hf
73	Tantalum	Ta
74	Tungsten	W
75	Rhenium	Re
76	Osmium	Os
77	Iridium	Ir
78	Platinum	Pt
79	Gold	Au
80	Mercury	Hg
81	Thallium	Tl
82	Lead	Pb
83	Bismuth	Bi
84	Polonium	Po
85	Astatine	At
86	Radon	Rn
87	Francium	Fr
88	Radium	Ra
89	Actinium	Ac
90	Thorium	Th
91	Protactinium	Pa
92	Uranium	U
93	Neptunium	Np
94	Plutonium	Pu
95	Americium	Am
96	Curium	Cm
97	Berkelium	Bk
98	Californium	Cf
99	Einsteinium	Es
100	Fermium	Fm
101	Mendelevium	Md
102	Nobelium	No
103	Lawrencium	Lr
104	Rutherfordium	Rf
105	Hahnium	Ha

IONIC COMPOUNDS

How atoms lose or gain electrons to become ions

Substances made of two or more elements joined together are called **compounds**. Table salt is a compound and is formed from the elements sodium and chlorine.

Salt is made up of atoms of sodium (Na) and chlorine (Cl). When salt dissolves, the sodium atoms lose electrons to the chlorine atoms. Positive sodium **ions** (Na^+) and negative chlorine ions (Cl^-) are formed. In a salt solution ions can move independently of each other.

If an atom gains one electron what sort of ion will it become?

Atoms from many different elements can gain or lose electrons to become ions. The compounds that these elements form are called **ionic compounds**. Ionic compounds usually have very high melting and boiling points. The positive and negative ions attract each other to form **ionic bonds**.

Sodium chloride has a high melting point.

An ionic compound is formed when electrons are transferred from one atom to another. The resulting substance can have quite different properties to the elements from which it is formed.

The rust on this rake is an ionic compound called hydrated iron oxide. Hydrated iron oxide is made up of iron ions, oxide ions and water.

Fertilizers contain the ionic compounds ammonium nitrate and potassium sulphate. Ammonium nitrate is made up of positively charged ammonium ions and negatively charged nitrate ions.

What are the ions in potassium sulphate?

When salt is dissolved in water, the ions from which salt is formed are free to move. This freedom of movement of charged particles allows the salt solution to conduct electricity. The positive ions (Na^+) are attracted to the negative electrode and the negative ions (Cl^-) to the positive. As the ions move through the salt solution they cause a current to flow.

What happens to the ions when an ionic compound dissolves in water?

The ions which form the ionic compound are deposited on the electrodes as the current flows. This is called an **electrolysis** reaction. As more and more of the ions become deposited, the solution becomes weaker and will eventually no longer conduct electricity.

What will be formed at the positive electrode?

In this electrolysis reaction the postively charged copper ions travel to the negative electrode where they are deposited as a very thin layer of pure copper.

What particles do the copper ions pick up at the negative electrode?

What might affect the speed at which copper is formed? Explain why.

If you had to test your prediction how would you do it?

Electrolysis is the process used to coat cutlery with silver. This thin silver coat is called silver plate.

Suggest a way of removing the silver plate from a fork.

SUMMARY

Ions are formed when atoms gain or lose electrons.

Ions can be positively or negatively charged.

An ionic compound is made of positive and negative ions attracted to each other.

A solution of an ionic compound conducts electricity and is decomposed by it.

MOLECULAR COMPOUNDS
How atoms share electrons to form molecules

Atoms of most elements don't normally exist on their own because they are **unstable.** Atoms combine with each other and become more **stable.**

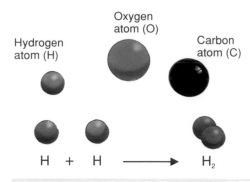

Hydrogen atom (H)

Oxygen atom (O)

Carbon atom (C)

Simple molecules are combinations of atoms of a single element. For example two hydrogen atoms can combine to form a molecule of hydrogen. The chemical symbol for a hydrogen atom is H. The chemical symbol for a hydrogen molecule is H_2.

H + H ⟶ H_2

What do you think the $_2$ stands for?

Atoms form molecules by sharing electrons. This creates a bond between the atoms. The bonds holding the atoms together in a molecule are strong. The forces holding groups of molecules together are weak.

Elements which form simple molecules, such as chlorine and hydrogen, are often gases.

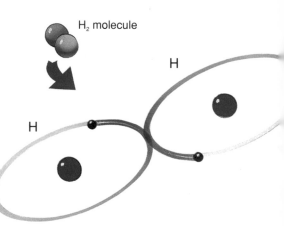

H_2 molecule

H

H

Atoms of different elements can combine to form molecules. Water is a molecular compound of hydrogen (H) and oxygen (O). The atoms of different elements can share different numbers of electrons. Hydrogen shares one but oxygen shares two. So when hydrogen and oxygen atoms combine to form a water molecule, two hydrogen atoms and one oxygen atom combine. The formula for water is H_2O.

What would a simple diagram of a water molecule look like?

Larger molecular compounds are often liquids or solids.

Sugar is a large molecular compound. It has the formula $C_6H_{12}O_6$.

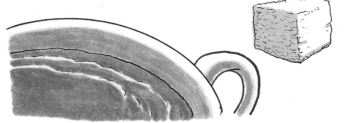

How many atoms are there in a sugar molecule?

What elements is a sugar molecule made from?

Ethene is a gas which is found in crude oil. The formula for ethene is C_2H_4.

Sometimes molecules combine to form extremely long molecules. **Plastics** are made up of long molecules.

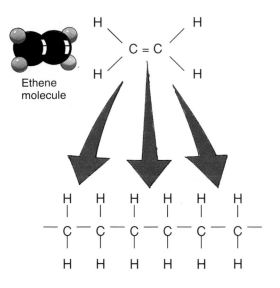

Ethene molecule

The plastic polythene is made of lots of ethene molecules bonded together. When simple molecules bond together like this, the new, bigger molecule is called a **polymer**.

Polyvinyl chloride (PVC) is a plastic made up of vinyl chloride molecules bonded together.

LP discs are made of PVC

What does a PVC molecule look like?

investigation

Pure molecular compounds do not conduct electricity because they do not contain charged particles. Water is a molecular compound. On its own it will not conduct electricity, but if a small amount of **acid** is added it will conduct electricity. This is because the acid turns the water molecules into ions (H^+ and OH^-).

When electricity is passed through water containing acid, bubbles of gas are seen at the electrodes. Hydrogen gas is seen at the negative electrode (**cathode**) and oxygen gas is seen at the positive electrode (**anode**).

Is more hydrogen or oxygen produced?

If 10 cm³ of hydrogen is given off what volume of oxygen is given off? Explain your answer.

SUMMARY

A molecule or molecular compound is formed when two or more atoms combine by sharing electrons.
Molecular compounds do not conduct electricity.

MIXTURES
How substances can be mixed and separated

A **mixture** is a blend of two or more substances which are not chemically bonded together. The proportions of the substances in a mixture are not fixed and are often easy to separate.

People have been putting steel and aluminium cans in the same can bank. There are too many cans to be separated by hand. The can collector knows steel is magnetic and aluminium is not.

Devise a simple machine to separate steel and aluminium cans.

If chalk and water are mixed together the particles of chalk do not dissolve but are dispersed in clusters throughout the liquid. This is called a **suspension** because the chalk is suspended in the water.

How could you separate the chalk and water?

An **emulsion** is a mixture of liquids. Emulsions are formed when tiny droplets of one liquid are spread through another liquid. Salad dressing is an emulsion.

Oil and vinegar are used as a salad dressing. These two liquids do not mix very well. Egg yolk is sometimes added to help them mix.

Oil and water have different densities. How could you separate a mixture of oil and vinegar?

Name another emulsion found in the home.

Oil Refinery

Investigation

Petrol

Kerosene

Diesel

Think of a way of separating and collecting all three of these chemicals.

Crude oil is a mixture of chemicals. An oil refinery is a factory which separates crude oil into petrol, diesel and other useful chemicals.

If crude oil is heated to 110 °C, petrol will evaporate from the mixture, leaving a mixture of kerosene and diesel behind.

Three useful chemicals obtained from crude oil are:

petrol   boiling point 110 °C
kerosene   boiling point 180 °C
diesel   boiling point 260 °C

SUMMARY

A mixture is made up of two or more substances which are not chemically bonded together.

The proportions of the components of a mixture are not fixed.

The components of a mixture are often easy to separate.

RADIOACTIVITY
How atoms give out rays and particles

Until the 20th century, atoms were generally thought to be tiny solid lumps which couldn't be broken down any further. The discovery of **radioactivity** helped to show that atoms are made up of a positive **nucleus** surrounded by a cloud of negatively charged electrons.

The nucleus is very small but weighs much more than the electrons. Most of the weight of an atom is concentrated in the nucleus. The nucleus itself is made up of particles called protons and neutrons. These are very similar except that protons have a positive charge but neutrons have no charge.

The more protons and neutrons there are in the nucleus, the heavier the atom will be.

In most atoms the nucleus is very stable. But some atoms have many more neutrons than protons and this tends to make them unstable. These atoms sometimes stabilize themselves by giving off particles. When this happens, the atom is said to be **radioactive**.

There are three types of radioactivity emitted from the nucleus of radioactive atoms. These are **alpha particles, beta particles** and **gamma rays.**

Alpha particles are made up of two neutrons and two protons.

Sometimes, a neutron decays to form a proton and an electron. When this happens, the fast moving electron is given off as a beta particle.

When a nucleus decays, it may be left with excess energy which will be emitted as a gamma ray.

Each type of radioactivity has a different ability to penetrate solid objects.

Would you expect the nucleus of an atom to be very dense? Can you explain why?

What would happen if the numbers of protons and electrons in an atom were not equal?

Carbon 14 is a form of radioactive carbon. It has 14 particles in its nucleus instead of the usual 12.

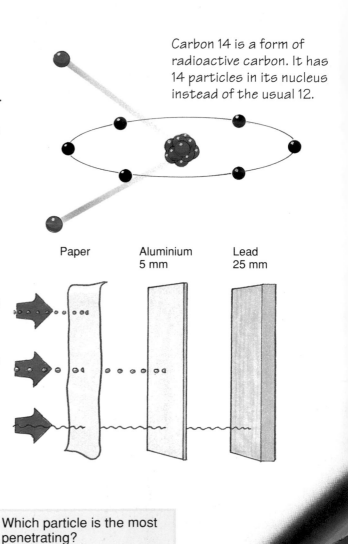

Which particle is the most penetrating?

Radioactivity can be detected with a **Geiger–Müller tube.**
When a radioactive particle enters the Geiger–Müller tube,
a clicking noise is heard. The radioactive particles that
enter the tube can be counted if the tube is connected to a
counting machine, known as a **Geiger counter**.

To amplifier

Path of particle

Geiger-Müller tube located in pick-up head

Geiger counter (and amplifier)

Pick-up head

Radioactive substances have
many uses. For example, the
thickness of paper can be
monitored, as it's produced,
by measuring how much
radiation passes through the
paper to a Geiger–Müller tube.

Paper measuring machine

Air, rocks and buildings all emit radiation.
Radiation from outer space arrives in the form
of **cosmic rays**. Background radiation from all
of these sources surrounds us all of the time.

What would happen if the paper
became extremely thin?

What type of particle should the
radioactive source emit to best
check the thickness of the paper?

Radiation is given off by
air, rocks and buildings

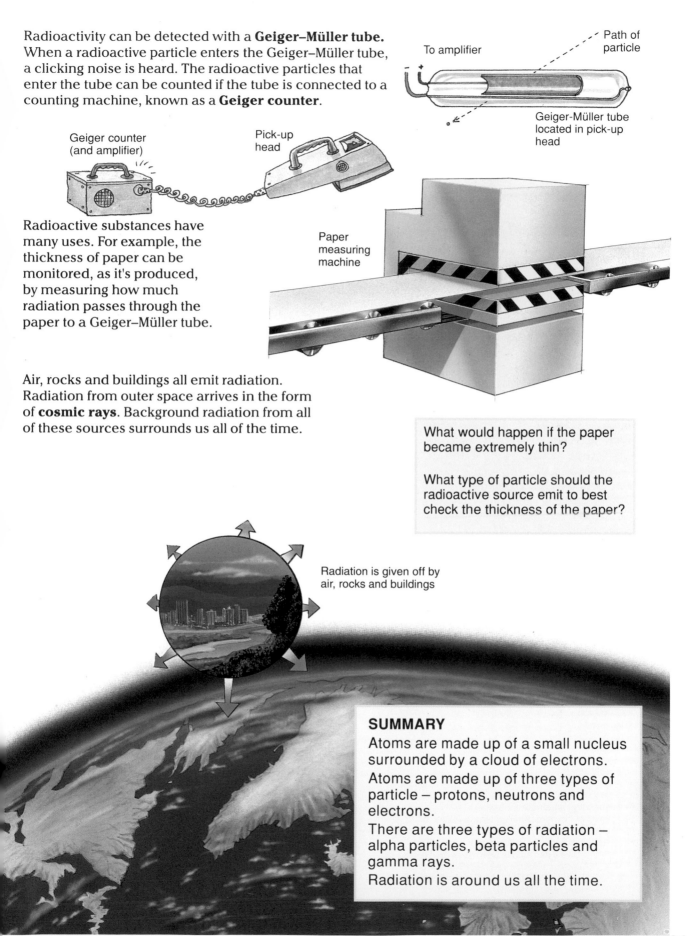

SUMMARY
Atoms are made up of a small nucleus
surrounded by a cloud of electrons.
Atoms are made up of three types of
particle – protons, neutrons and
electrons.
There are three types of radiation –
alpha particles, beta particles and
gamma rays.
Radiation is around us all the time.

Key words appear in **bold** the first time
they occur in the text.

INDEX

Published by Heinemann Library,
an imprint of Heinemann Publishers (Oxford) Ltd,
Halley Court, Jordan Hill, Oxford, OX2 8EJ

OXFORD LONDON EDINBURGH
MADRID PARIS ATHENS BOLOGNA
MELBOURNE SYDNEY AUCKLAND SINGAPORE
TOKYO IBADAN NAIROBI GABORONE HARARE
PORTSMOUTH NH (USA)

© Lazy Summer Books Ltd. 1994
First published 1994
98 97 96 95 94
10 9 8 7 6 5 4 3 2 1
British Library Cataloguing Publication in Data
is available on request from the British Library.
ISBN 0-431-07603-0 (HB)
ISBN 0-431-07565-4 (PB)
Designed by Lazy Summer Books Ltd.
Illustrated by Lazy Summer Books Ltd.
Printed and bound in China